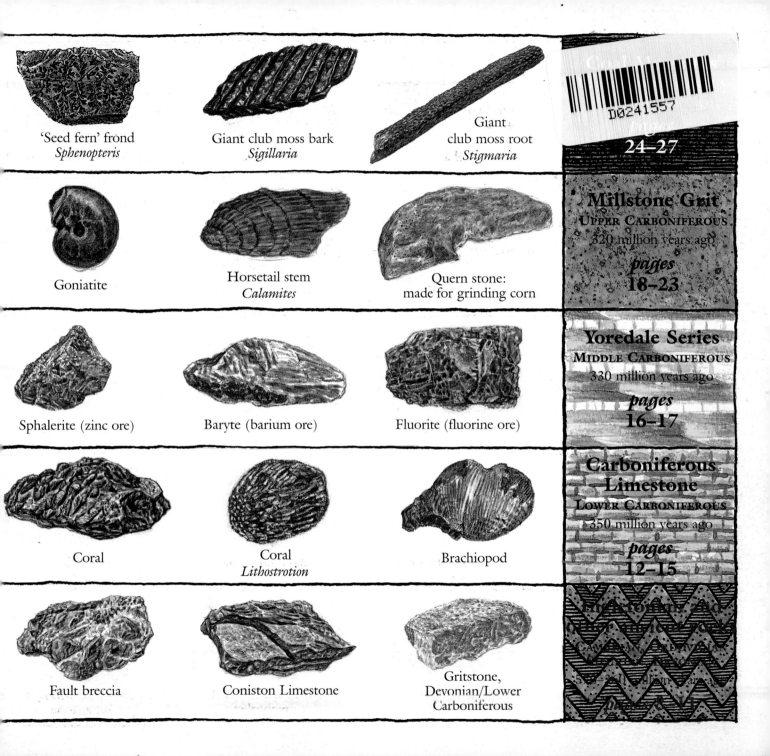

'Seed fern' frond
Sphenopteris

Giant club moss bark
Sigillaria

Giant
club moss root
Stigmaria

D0241557

pages
24–27

Goniatite

Horsetail stem
Calamites

Quern stone:
made for grinding corn

Sphalerite (zinc ore)

Baryte (barium ore)

Fluorite (fluorine ore)

Coral

Coral
Lithostrotion

Brachiopod

Fault breccia

Coniston Limestone

Gritstone,
Devonian/Lower
Carboniferous

Sand dunes,
Spurn Head

Ice Age Boulder
Clay on Cretaceous
Chalk, Thornwick Bay,
Flamborough

Ice Age drumlins, near
Hellifield

Jurassic sandstone,
Roman Road, Goathland,
North York Moors

Permian Magnesian
Limestone walls of York

Cophouse Colliery,
Coal Measures

Millstone Grit wall,
Haworth Moor

Limestone Scars,
Yoredale Series,
slopes of Pen-y-ghent

◄ Carboniferous Limestone,
Stump Cross Caverns

Folded Silurian greywacke,
Old Arcow Quarry,
Horton-in-Ribblesdale

Yorkshire

CRAVEN COLLEGE

AB
AB

H17320
911

544.1
911

544.1

This book is to be returned on or before
the last date stamped below

- 1 NOV 2004
1 5 NOV 2004
1 6 APR 2007
- 5 NOV 2007
2 0 MAR 2009

2 6 FEB 2010
2 5 NOV 2010
4 FEB 2011

2014

Ammonite . Jurassic . Whitby .

Written and illustrated by

Richard Bell

British Geological Survey
1835

◀ Yorkshire's Rocks form the
basis of Yorkshire's landscapes
and buildings: in this montage
the oldest rocks are at the
bottom, the youngest at the top.

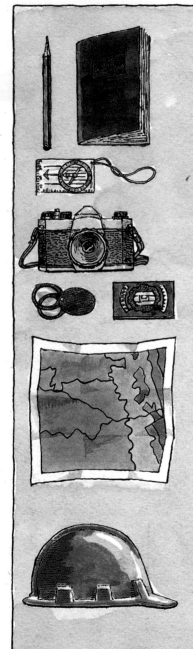

Code for Fieldwork

- Use a notebook and camera rather than a hammer.

- Don't be greedy when collecting. Rocks, fossils and landforms need conservation, just like wildlife. Some sites are protected by law.

- If you are hammering, please break loose rocks and fallen material. Don't attack rock faces. It is best to leave fossils and other features in the rock face, so that they can be seen by others in their true setting.

- Take care when hammering. Pyritised ammonites, for example, smash into razor-sharp splinters. Yorkshire geologist Adam Sedgwick lost an eye as he hammered one out at Robin Hood's Bay. Safety goggles give some protection.

- Quarries and cliffs can be dangerous. William Smith, a pioneer of Yorkshire geology, lost the use of a leg after a fall from Castle Hill, Scarborough.

- Many sea cliffs are unstable, and, while a hard hat gives useful protection, it is of little use in a big rock fall.

- Some bays are completely cut off well before high tide. It is safest to explore them on a falling tide.

- If you keep a collection, make a note of exactly where you found a specimen. The date is also useful, as some sites are soon filled in or overgrown. Write on the specimen using Indian ink if possible.

- National grid references are given for the sites in this book, but this does not imply that all sites have public access.

For Tom, who brings geology to life

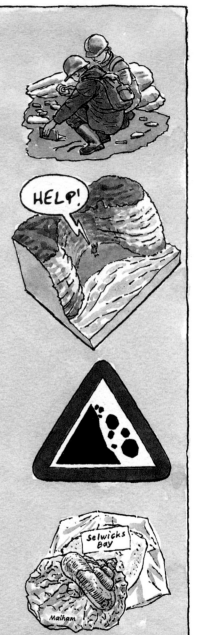

Contents

Journey through Time

What was Yorkshire like before man arrived on the scene?

Everywhere there are clues in the rocks;

- **Barnsley** — a steamy, tropical forest

- **Doncaster** — a hot, sandy desert

- **Scarborough** — the dinosaur's delta

- **York** — in the shadow of a glacier

How could all this happen here in Yorkshire?

One answer is **continental drift**. Like the rest of the world, our part of the Earth's crust is on the move. Every year, new sea floor is created at volcanic vents along an underwater ridge in the middle of the Atlantic. Every year we move a few centimetres further away from North America.

Over millions of years these few centimetres of movement have added up to thousands of kilometres. During the last 500 million years we have moved from some 5000 kilometres south of the equator to over 5000 kilometres north.

During this time we've moved through the planet's climatic zones: we've passed through two desert belts and the region of tropical forest between; on several occasions we've been flooded by warm tropical seas and we are now so far north that ice age glaciers have 'recently' moved across the county on several occasions.

Record of the Rocks

THIS IS THE STORY of Yorkshire's voyage through time as it is told in the rocks, fossils and landforms of the county. This book shows you where to look and what to look for. Wherever you are, on a beach, in the hills, or on a city street, there are clues to the lost worlds that were once right here, on your doorstep. Pick up a pebble and you are reaching back millions of years in time.

If we could find all of Yorkshire's rocks in one cliff face they would look something like this (see right). As William 'Strata' Smith put it, the layers look like a pile of bread and butter sandwiches.

There are layers of honey-coloured sandstone, creamy-white limestone and dark sticky clay. Some layers are crammed with the remnants of primitive forest giants, while others are jam-packed with fossil sea shells.

Some rocks are hard, like the millstone grit which is tough enough to put an edge on Sheffield steel. Others, like shales, desert sands and ice age clays are so soft that they may crumble in your hand.

There probably isn't anywhere in Yorkshire where you can find the whole sequence of rocks together like this imaginary cliff face even if you bored down through the ground. Earth movements have folded, faulted and tilted the layers. Parts of the story are missing altogether. At times tens of millions of years have gone by, leaving scarcely a trace in the rocky record.

When our story starts, 500 million years ago, what would one day be Yorkshire lay on the bed of an ocean...

The Lost Ocean

ORDOVICIAN AND SILURIAN PERIODS, 500–400 MILLION
YEARS AGO

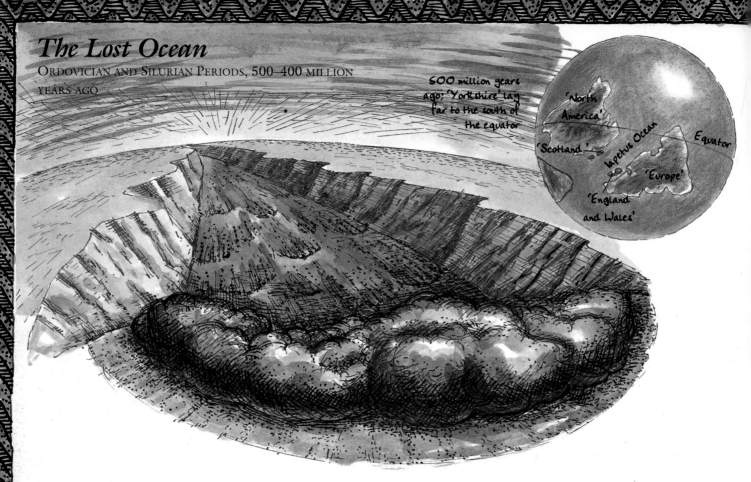

500 million years ago: 'Yorkshire' lay far to the south of the equator

'North America'

'Scotland'

Iapetus Ocean

Equator

'Europe'

'England and Wales'

'Scotland'

'Yorkshire'

'England and Wales'

Iapetus Ocean

Subduction zone

Our part of the Earth's crust lay on the bed of an ocean.

A DISTANT EARTHQUAKE causes a tremor that shakes the sea bed. Layers of mud and sand stacked up on the continental shelf start to cascade down at 70 kilometres an hour along an underwater canyon to the ocean bed below. When this turns to rock it makes a tough muddy-coloured sandstone called greywacke.

This is how the oldest rocks in Yorkshire were formed. Our part of the Earth's crust then lay far to the south of the equator on the floor of the lost ocean of Iapetus, which was closing, vanishing. (In Greek mythology Iapetus was the father of Atlas; the Iapetus Ocean was later reborn as the Atlantic).

The continents were moving towards one another at about the speed that your fingernails grow. As they collided, the friction of the collision slowly produced molten rocks or magma such as granite. One of these granite magmas solidified deep under Wensleydale.

8

The avalanche produces **greywacke**, a mixture of sand and clay.

Sand grains   XS

Between the avalanches, in calm water, fine mud settles on the ocean floor. This turns into **mudstone** and **shale**.

X100   Fine mud particles

Make an underwater avalanche

- Put a handful of mixed-up grit, sand and soil into an old coffee jar.
- Add water until two-thirds full.
- Screw on the lid and shake.
- Leave to settle until the water is clear.
- Which settles out first—sand, grit or mud?

Caledonian CRUNCH!

As the continents collided these ocean bed rocks were caught between the two land masses. The layers of greywacke and mudstone were crumpled into folds.

'North America'   Caledonian mountains   'Europe'

400 million years ago: Caledonian mountains.

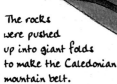

The rocks were pushed up into giant folds to make the Caledonian mountain belt.

Pressure turned shale into slate.

Greywacke

Rocks came under great pressure as they were folded. Clayey minerals in the shale were re-aligned and recrystallised to form a new metamorphic rock called **slate**, typical of the Ingletonian rocks found near Ingleton, North Yorkshire.

Slate

Clocks in the Rocks

Just how old are Yorkshire's oldest rocks?

Fossils

Smith was the first to realise that remains of past life, like this extinct sea creature, can be used to date the rocks. The older the rock, the more primitive are its life forms.

Fossil graptolite

Relative Dating

Pioneer geologist and canal engineer William Smith (1769–1839) said that the rocks of Yorkshire are like a plate of bread and butter sandwiches. The slices of bread are layers of hard rock and the butter the softer layers between. The oldest sandwiches (or rocks) are those at the bottom of the pile. Often the whole pile gets tilted over.

Newer rocks lie on top of the upturned older rocks

Atomic clock

Some unstable atoms change to more stable forms, giving off a small burst of energy, known as radioactivity. Scientists measure the amount of radioactive decay in a rock to give a date in years. For instance, radioactive potassium decays into calcium plus a gas, argon, at a slow and steady rate. Half will have changed after 12 billion years.

The Ingletonian rocks have no large fossils, they contain little radioactive material and there is a huge gap in time before the next layer of rocks was laid on top. Dates between 400 million years and 600 million years have been suggested.

◀ **Pecca Falls** [SD 695 749] -- hard greywacke, softer slate

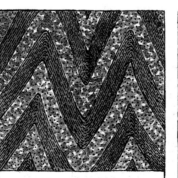

Layers of sandy greywacke and muddy shale were folded when continents collided. Pressure turned the shale to slate.

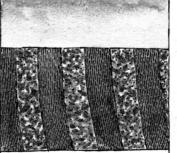

Today, near Ingleton, layers of sandy greywacke and fine-grained slate can be seen tipped on end. These rocks are known as the INGLETONIAN.

At Pecca Falls, tough greywacke forms each waterfall. Slate, which splits easily, forms the deep plunge pools.

10

Where to see Yorkshire's oldest rocks

North Craven Fault

Slate clapper bridge in CRUMMACKDALE [SD 776 705]

Malham Tarn [SD 895 665] ▶
A block of old ocean bed rocks, covered with boulder clay, makes a waterproof bed for the tarn. Water flowing out of the tarn soon sinks into potholes in the younger limestone.

Dry Rigg Quarry
Helwith Bridge [SD 804 692]
Roadstone quarries in folded ocean bed rocks of the Silurian period.

Thornton Force [SD 695 754]
A blanket of white limestone lies over the old upended ocean bed rocks. Under the overhanging lip of the waterfall, stuck in the bottom of the limestone, there are big pebbles of Ingletonian rocks. 360 million years ago they were part of a tropical beach which was later submerged by the limestone sea.

White Scar Caves
[SD 713 745]
At the entrance you can see the old folded Ingletonian rocks. The cave is in the limestone above.

Old Red Desert

DEVONIAN, 410 TO 360 MILLION YEARS AGO

As the world's continents moved towards each other, our part of the Earth's crust became a desert. The Caledonian fold mountains were worn down in a hot dry climate with occasional flash floods.

Deep desert basins would one day be flooded by sea water. The higher ground between them would become islands. By the time the limestone of Malham Cove was laid down these islands too had been submerged. They became shallow lagoons, surrounded by reefs.

Adam Sedgwick (1785-1873) studied the rocks near his childhood home of Dent. In the Howgill Fells he found old ocean rocks, like those of the Lake District.

Sedbergh, 400 million years ago. The old red desert has left few traces in Yorkshire. The remains of a wadi filled with rocky debris can be seen on the Sedgwick Geological Trail near Sedbergh.

Image labels: Cladoselache, Brachiopod, Corals, Bryozoan Fan, Brachiopods, Seaweed, Algae, Crinoid

Life on the Reef

EARLY CARBONIFEROUS, 350 MILLION YEARS AGO

YORKSHIRE, 350 MILLION YEARS AGO. **A shallow tropical lagoon** covers most of the Dales which are ringed about by reefs rich in marine life.

Crinoid

Crinoidal limestone is packed with stem fragments.

Crinoids spread their arms in the currents which sweep up the reef slope. The crinoid is sometimes described as a sea lily because it looks like a flower. It is really an animal, built like an upside-down starfish on a stick. Waving tentacles on the arms pass food particles along grooves to a central mouth.

Like many reef animals, the crinoid has a skeleton of lime. It extracts dissolved lime, calcium carbonate, from seawater to make a skeleton of armour plates and beads.

Algal limestone

Algae are the main reef builders. They are small plants which grow best on the crest of the reef, and form spreading mats.

Straparollus

Sea snails, and other molluscs with shells like those of oysters and clams, live on or in the limy ooze of the reef. Their broken-up shells, along with corals and crinoid skeletons, add to the bulk of the reef.

Brachiopods are filter-feeders with thick shells; some have stalks or spines to keep them anchored in the mud.

Lithostrotion

Corals build cups and platforms of lime. Some live alone and form a skeleton shaped like a horn, while others live in root-like colonies.

Rugose coral

Bryozoans build colonies shaped like nets and fans.

Goniatite

Nautiloid

Conodont   Trilobite

Brachiopod

13

Block and basin

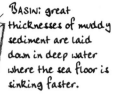

REEF KNOLL grows upwards while the sea floor is slowly sinking. Algae which build the reef need sunlight to live.

BASIN: great thicknesses of muddy sediment are laid down in deep water where the sea floor is sinking faster.

SHELF and LAGOON where a shallow sea covers a block of older rocks.

350 million years ago; drifting continents cause a stretching of the Earth's crust in 'Yorkshire'. In some places the crust sinks to form basins. Between the basins there are blocks of higher ground.

SHELF LIMESTONE, from the lagoon, is white and is found in regular layers.

REEF LIMESTONE, also white, has no regular layers and is full of shelly debris.

BASIN LIMESTONE is dark because of its mud and oil content. A fresh piece smells of oil.

Limestone Story

It is easy to extract lime from water. When limy (hard) water is boiled in a kettle it leaves a scum of limescale.

Sea creatures first started making shells and skeletons of lime about 600 million years ago. They extract the lime from sea water.

The limestone of the Yorkshire Dales is made up mainly of the crushed shells and skeletons of sea creatures.

Stump Cross Cavern [SE 089 635]

Limestone is a hard rock but rainwater and groundwater can dissolve it. Both are slightly acidic. When water evaporates in caves and waterfalls, the lime can be deposited again as stalactites, stalagmites, dripstone or tufa.

Cracks and Caves

Yorkshire, 350 million years ago: in the shallow tropical seas layers of white chalky mud are laid down.

As the mud changes to limestone, it shrinks causing cracks, called joints, which split the layers from top to bottom.

280 million years ago: Earth movements cause long cracks, called master joints, which run north west to south east across the limestone.

Water finds its way down through the joints and along the bedding planes between the layers. Potholes and caves develop.

Limestone Country

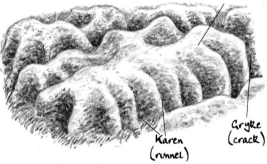

Clint (block)

Gryke (crack)

Karen (runnel)

Limestone pavement develops on the almost flat beds of limestone in the Dales. Because limestone is so pure most of the rock dissolves away leaving little mud or sand to form soil. Glaciers scraping over the limestone in the last ice age may have started the process off, leaving a flat surface of bare rock.

Kilnsey Crag, a limestone scar in Wharfedale. [SD 974 681]

Gordale Scar, like nearby Malham Cove, is made of a thick layer of limestone from the shelf sea. [SD 915 640]

Stebden Hill, one of several reef knolls near Cracoe, keeps the shape it had when it grew as a reef on the sea floor. [SD 997 609]

Gaping Gill: probably the best known pothole in Britain. The cave below is big enough to swallow York Minster. [SD 752 727]

Ingleborough Cave was once an exit for the stream which plunges underground at Gaping Gill, 1.5 kilometres to the north. [SD 754 711]

15

Fits and Starts

MIDDLE CARBONIFEROUS, 330 MILLION YEARS AGO

T HE GREAT LIMESTONE SEA would, one day, become choked up with mud and sand. A great river delta was spreading south, draining land in the north. But the sea didn't disappear all at once. It would flood the new river delta again and again over the next few million years...

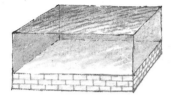

1 Limestone is laid down in a clear sea.

2 Mud washed from distant land settles in calm conditions.

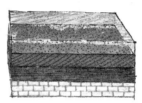

3 Rivers bring sand from the land to the north.

4 Swampy forest grows on top of the river delta.

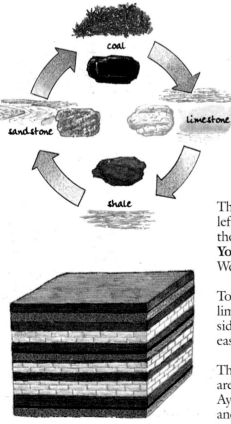

coal

limestone

sandstone

shale

As they are buried, shelly debris changes to limestone, mud changes to shale, sand to sandstone and peat to coal. As the Earth's crust subsides, the sea floods in and the cycle starts all over again, beginning with the limestone.

This happened at least eight times, but often one or more stages in the cycle is missing. For instance the thin coal seam at the end of the cycle may be absent. River deltas change shape as old channels become blocked by sand, so the rocks vary from place to place.

This long battle between land and sea has left a 'layer cake' of hard and soft rocks in the northern dales. They are called the **Yoredale Series**, after the old name for Wensleydale, the valley of the Ure.

Today the harder rocks, especially limestone, form steep steps along the valley sides, while the soft shales have been more easily worn away as shallow slopes.

The Yoredale Series limestone and shales are especially rich in fossils. Vistors to Aysgarth can see many compound corals and large *Productus* brachiopods.

Steps, Scars and Shafts

Where to see the Yoredale Series

The long scars on the valley sides in **Wensleydale** [SD 881 923] are layers of limestone. It has cut deeper and exposed more limestones than in Swaledale, to the north.

The stepped sides of **Pen-y-Ghent** are limestones and shales of the Yoredale Series. They rest on a thick, flat bed of earlier shelf limestone. [SD 838 734]

Lead Mining

Hard Level Gill. [NY 974 005]

Hardraw Force shows a range of Yoredale rocks: limestone forms the top of the fall, shale the plunge pool, with a cliff face of sandstone between. [SD 869 916]

In many places in the dales mineral veins are found in joints (cracks) in the limestone. In **Swaledale** there are levels, shafts and rakes (large trenches) dug for galena (lead ore). Other minerals such as sphalerite, baryte, calcite and fluorite were dumped on spoil heaps as gangue (waste). Recently fluorite has been worked from old dumps.

At **Aysgarth Falls** the 'steps' are hard beds of limestone near the base of the Yoredale Series. [SE 009 884]

The **Buttertubs** are potholes eroded into one of the thicker layers of Yoredale Series limestone. [SD 874 961]

Hushing was a spectacular process where dammed-up water was released to cut ravines, exposing seams of lead ore.

THE WORLD IN A GRAIN OF SAND

Every grain of sand has a story to tell...

It begins with an exploding star.

New elements, formed from hydrogen and helium, are thrown off into space.

Two of these elements, silicon and oxygen make up much of the crust of the newly-formed planet Earth.

Granite is a common rock in the crust.

It forms as a molten magma deep below mountains. At the surface magma appears as lava.

As the melt cools, rock crystals form. They all contain silicate - a combination of silicon and oxygen, along with other elements such as iron and aluminium.

Quartz is the last crystal to form. It is pure silica (SiO_2) combining silicon (Si) and oxygen (O_2).

Si O_2

The atoms are strongly bonded to make quartz the toughest of the common rock forming minerals

The shape of a perfect quartz crystal reflects its atomic structure.

But the quartz in granite fills the spaces between the other crystals. It looks like crushed ice.

Rain, wind and chemical attack all help to break up the rock.

Rock falls, soil creep, glaciers, streams, rivers and wind help transport the debris.

Mud and sand are deposited in rivers, lakes, dunes and on the sea bed.

Rock   Pebbles   Gravel   Grit   Sand

Rock fragments are ground up on their journey. Some crystals, such as feldspar, soon decompose to clay but quartz survives as quartz sand.

Look closely at sand; abrasion during transport has rounded the grains; desert sand is wind-polished; the rounder the grain, the longer it has been in transport.

Coarse sand was laid down under water by strong currents.

When layers of sand are buried and compressed the sand grains lock closer together.

Water is squeezed out...

...leaving a residue of iron, lime or silica, which cements the grains together and turns loose sand into a solid rock: SANDSTONE.

From Mountains to Millstones

You can often find little pebbles of quartz in Millstone Grit. Pebbles are laid down by faster-flowing water.

A MIGHTY RIVER washes grit and sand into a delta that covers half of Yorkshire.

Granite mountains in the north are worn down quickly by tropical rainstorms. Swift rivers soon take rocky debris to the delta. As soon as one layer of sand and grit (coarse sand) is laid down, more comes along. There isn't even time for shellfish to settle on the sand before the next load is dumped. Rock crystals of feldspar, which normally turns to clay quite quickly, are buried along with lots of tough quartz.

Today, 320 million years later, this has become the tough sandstone known as Millstone Grit, which makes up much of the Pennines and is its main building stone.

Gritstone Cycle

320 million years ago; the sea floor sinks.

An avalanche of mixed-up mud and sand covers the seabed.

Mud, suspended in the water, settles out slowly.

Silt and sand are washed in as the front of a delta advances.

River channels dump sand. Sand and mud banks build up.

Forests grow on top of the delta. Coal seams may be produced.

The sea floor sinks and the whole process starts again.

The Earth's crust acts like a see-saw, as rocky material moves from the mountains to the delta.

Stripped of the weight, the mountains rise while the sea bed subsides.

Worldwide, the sea level sometimes rises, flooding the deltas. One invasion of the sea leaves a layer of dark mud only a few centimetres thick but stretching from Ireland to Russia.

Russia
Yorkshire
Ireland

Fossils in these marine bands include GONIATITES, extinct relatives of the squid, octopus and ammonite.

Brimham Rocks [SE 210 650]

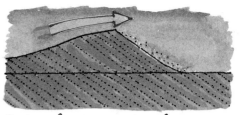

Sand was often laid down layer after layer in underwater dunes.

Cross-bedding, joints and bedding planes at Brimham Rocks.

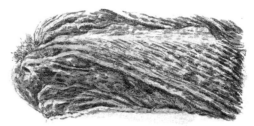

Erosion has picked out these layers, which slant across each bed and are therefore called CROSS-BEDDING.

Although Millstone Grit is tough, it has lines of weakness.

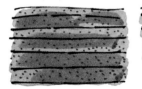

1. There are BEDDING PLANES between the layers of rock.

2. And vertical JOINTS.

3. Rain, wind, ice and sun attack the rock along these bedding planes and joints.

4. Soon after the last glaciation the land is bare of plant cover.

5. Strong winds bounce sand grains along close to ground level, where sand-blasting is most effective.

6. If there are soft layers of rock at ground level, sandblasting can produce a mushroom-shaped rock.

Idol Rock

Gritstone Country

Cow and Calf, Ilkley [SE 129 469]
At gritstone edges such as Ilkley Moor, the gritstone lies on top of soft layers of shale. As the shale is worn away the gritstone splits along vertical joints. Huge blocks break off and, like the Calf, slide downhill.

Millstone Edge, Hathersage [SK 248 806]
Here, overlooking Derbyshire, the pattern of joints and bedding planes allowed quarrymen to split the gritstone into blocks roughly the size of a millstone. Feldspar crystals in the rock wear quicker than the quartz, and this hardness contrast ensures the grinding surface of the millstone keeps its 'tooth' and never gets polished smooth.

Fragment of quern stone for grinding corn by hand.

Quartz pebbles in gritstone.

Blackstone Edge, [SD 973 170] Millstone Grit slabs pave a mysterious 'Roman Road'.

The Millstone Grit outcrop in Yorkshire.

Richmond
Hawes
Skipton
Harrogate
Hebden Bridge
Huddersfield
Holmfirth
Sheffield

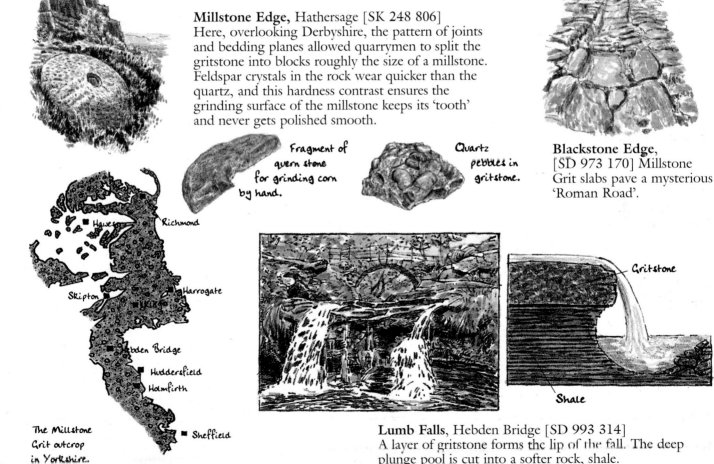

Gritstone
Shale

Lumb Falls, Hebden Bridge [SD 993 314]
A layer of gritstone forms the lip of the fall. The deep plunge pool is cut into a softer rock, shale.

23

BLACK FOREST

Cordaites

Giant horsetail

Barnsley, 300 million years ago...

The greatest tropical forest the world has ever seen stretches from North America to Europe.

With neither birds nor mammals the forests are quiet, perhaps silent...

Sphenophyllum

...even the dinosaurs have not yet appeared.

Giant club moss

Giant club mosses grow to the height of pylons. They have massive pillar-like trunks and tiny scale-like leaves.

Pholiderpeton

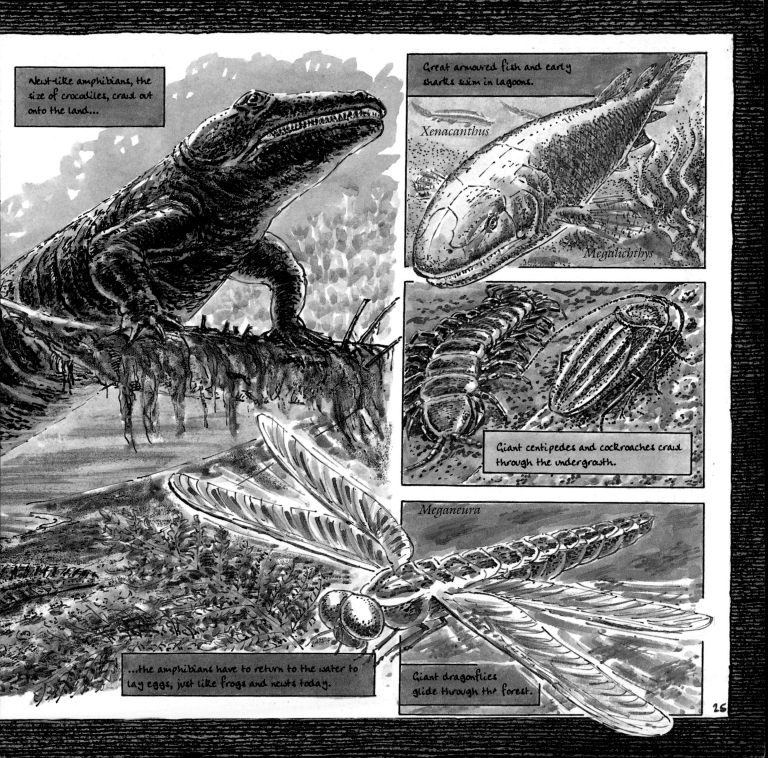

Newt-like amphibians, the size of crocodiles, crawl out onto the land...

Great armoured fish and early sharks swim in lagoons.

Xenacanthus

Megalichthys

Giant centipedes and cockroaches crawl through the undergrowth.

Meganeura

...the amphibians have to return to the water to lay eggs, just like frogs and newts today.

Giant dragonflies glide through the forest.

Coal Forest Fossils

Giant club moss *Lepidodendron*

Seed fern cone
Trigonocarpus

Giant club moss leaves *Lepidodendron*

Although plants are rare in the fossil record, Coal is composed entirely of plant remains. In coal fossils we get a rare glimpse of the first great forest.

Even in the Coal Measures, the remains of plants are usually widely scattered. Roots are found in fossil soil; trunks are sometimes buried in river sand; branches, leaves and cones might be blown or washed away.

Giant club moss bark
Lepidodendron

Giant club moss bark
Sigillaria

Giant club moss roots

Stigmaria

The dots are scars where rootlets were attached

Marine bands

A freshwater clam, *Carbonicola*, *(right)* lived as a filter-feeder in the mud of the lakes and lagoons. At times the sea swept in across the coal swamps leaving a marine band, a layer including fossil sea shells such as the brachiopod *Lingula*, which has survived, little changed, to the present day.

Forest, river, lake, lagoon, sea

Flooded forest
Forest
Lake
Lagoon
River
Forest fire
Sea

From the air the coal forests looked like today's Amazon delta or the Florida Everglades. Because of the mix of forest, lake, lagoon, river and sea, we now have a mix of rock types; coal, mudstone, sandstone and marine bands.

Coal　　　Mudstone　　　Sandstone

The Yorkshire Coalfield

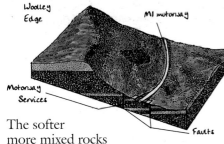

The softer more mixed rocks of the Coal Measures produce a gentler landscape than the Millstone Grit. **Woolley Edge** [SE 307 135] produces a bold scarp because the Coal Measures sandstone here is unusually gritty.

Visit an **opencast mine** and you will see why the Coal Measures are sometimes called the *grey* measures.

Most of Yorkshire's deep mines have now closed but you can still visit **Caphouse Colliery**, Overton, now the National Coal Mining Museum. [SE 253 165]

Ironstone

Iron carbonate deposited among the lake muds gives layers and nodules of ironstone. Medieval monks worked the Tankersley ironstone at Tankersley, South Yorkshire, and Emley, West Yorkshire.

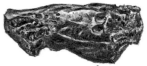

Furnace slag from near Emley

Tankersley iron workings [SK 353 986]

Old King Coal

Opencast mining dumper

Medieval monks, used charcoal to smelt iron

Collier, Middleton, 1814

World's first railway, Middleton, Leeds (1758); steam locomotives introduced 1812

Child labour in mines, banned 1842

Pit ponies: used in Yorkshire until the 1970s.

Deep mining reduced from 72 to 10 pits in Yorkshire, 1971-1996.

27

Pangaea, Supercontinent

UPPER CARBONIFEROUS TO PERMIAN PERIODS; VARISCAN MOUNTAIN BUILDING, 280 MILLION YEARS AGO

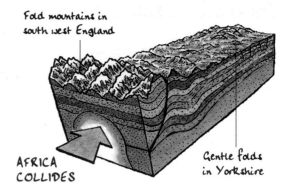

Fold mountains in south west England

AFRICA COLLIDES

Gentle folds in Yorkshire

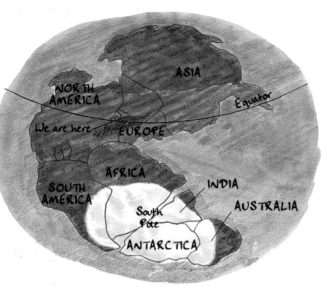

Continental drift brings all the world's continents together 280 million years ago. The supercontinent Pangaea (from the Greek for 'all the Earth') is the biggest land mass the world has ever known (left).

Africa drifts in from the south. New fold mountains the size of the Himalayas are thrust up across parts of Europe and south west England. The collision is felt as far away as Yorkshire, where it produces the Pennine Anticline.

Dales Earthquakes

South Craven Fault

Askrigg Block

As Pangaea comes together, there are massive earthquakes as the rocks crack along **faults**.

Giggleswick Scar [SD 793 659]
Earthquakes along the South Craven Fault have moved up the land (Askrigg Block) to the north east of the A65 road. Since Pangaea came together there has been hundreds of metres of vertical movement along this fault.

Faults remain as lines of weakness. There was a small earthquake on the South Craven Fault in 1944.

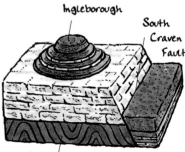

Ingleborough

South Craven Fault

Askrigg block

Today many of the uplifted rocks have been eroded away, leaving isolated remnants such as Ingleborough, Pen-y-Ghent and Whernside: the Three Peaks.

Pennine Anticline

The limestone, Millstone Grit and Coal Measures of the south Pennines are laid down in flat, almost level, beds.

280 million years ago, the layers are pushed up into a shallow dome called an anticline. This upfold is much higher than the Pennines of today.

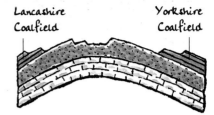

Over millions of years, the top layers of the dome are worn away, separating the Yorkshire and Lancashire coal fields, and exposing the Millstone Grit of today's Pennines.

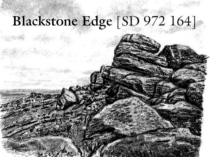

Blackstone Edge [SD 972 164]

Like most Millstone Grit outcrops on the Yorkshire slopes of the Pennines, the beds dip gently to the east.

Measuring Dip and Strike

1 Trickle water onto an exposed bedding plane in the rock.

2 The direction in which it flows is the dip.

3 Using a compass, find the direction of dip.

4 Measure the angle of dip using a clinometer (available from geologists' suppliers) or an angle finder (from DIY stores).

5 The dip is at right angles to the strike: the trend of a horizontal line on the surface.

Dying Sea

PERMIAN PERIOD 290–245 MILLION YEARS AGO

Leeds, 270 million years ago: the rocks are stained red and sand dunes build up along the sides of the newly-formed Pennines. These dunes, made of rounded and wind-polished sand, will later be mined at Pontefract. Britain is locked into the desert belt of the supercontinent Pangaea that lasted for 70 million years. Fifteen million years later: the shallow, tropical, Zechstein Sea floods the sand dunes and laps against the Pennines. Not far from shore there is a string of low reefs built by filter-feeding bryozoans and tiny primitive plants, the algae.

This **Zechstein Sea** stretched from Leeds to Germany and Poland. There was only a narrow connection with the world ocean (Panthalassa) which surrounded Pangaea. Cut off from the ocean, the sea became more and more salty, like the Arabian Gulf today. Limestone on the sea floor, formed in the normal way (see page 14), but became enriched in magnesium concentrated in the salty water.

IN MAGNESIAN LIMESTONE, dolomite, a double carbonate of magnesium and calcium, $CaMg(CO_3)_2$, is present. The rock is usually a creamy-yellow colour.

Horridonia horrida, a filter-feeding brachiopod. Marine life died out as the sea became more salty.

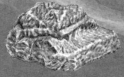

GYPSUM formed in salty seas and lagoons. It is often found with marl.

MARL is made up of desert dust that settled in shallow water; it is limy clay.

Going . . .   going . . .   . . . gone!

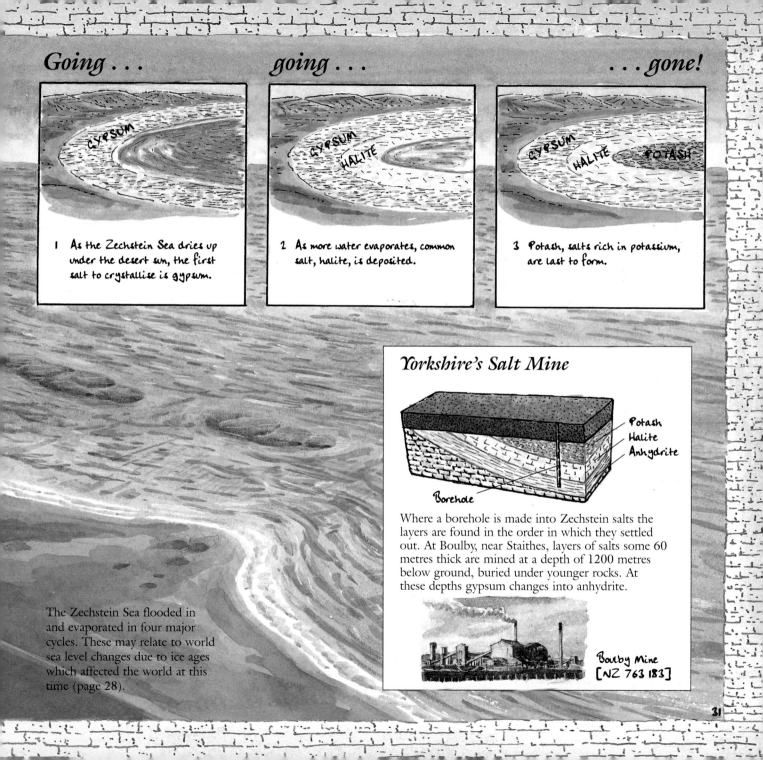

1 As the Zechstein Sea dries up under the desert sun, the first salt to crystallise is gypsum.

2 As more water evaporates, common salt, halite, is deposited.

3 Potash, salts rich in potassium, are last to form.

Yorkshire's Salt Mine

Where a borehole is made into Zechstein salts the layers are found in the order in which they settled out. At Boulby, near Staithes, layers of salts some 60 metres thick are mined at a depth of 1200 metres below ground, buried under younger rocks. At these depths gypsum changes into anhydrite.

Boulby Mine
[NZ 763 183]

The Zechstein Sea flooded in and evaporated in four major cycles. These may relate to world sea level changes due to ice ages which affected the world at this time (page 28).

Red Desert TRIASSIC PERIOD 245–210 MILLION YEARS AGO

A desert storm, 240 million years ago

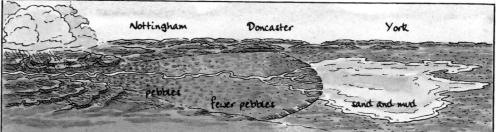

A flash flood washes debris into a desert basin. Pebbles are carried along in fast flowing water; sand and mud are deposited as the flood spreads more gently across the basin floor.

Ripple marks in Sherwood Sandstone, from a borehole near Doncaster, indicate shallow water.

Sherwood Sandstone (previously known as Bunter Sandstone).

Lakes and salt pans form in the desert basin.

Pangaea

220 million years ago: the supercontinent starts to break up. World sea level rises again as massive volcanic activity resumes along new mid-ocean ridges.

As Pangaea splits a shallow sea again extends across the desert.

Scarp and Vale
MAGNESIAN LIMESTONE AND DESERT ROCKS IN YORKSHIRE

Wetherby on the A1 road.

There are few villages on the Magnesian Limestone where surface water supplies are hard to find.

York; the walls and Minster are built of magnesian limestone.

Tadcaster

Vale of York

Selby concealed coalfield.

Yorkshire Coalfield

Coal Measures

Magnesian Limestone

Desert sandstone and marl

TOWTON CROSS, on the limestone ridge near Tadcaster, marks the site of the bloodiest battle of the Wars of the Roses in 1461. [SE 477 385]

The Romans used the magnesian limestone ridge for their road. The Great North Road, the modern A1, follows it too. The steep scarp slope of the ridge looks west over the older Coal Measures. The gentle dip slope goes down to the Vale of York to the east.

Soft red sandstone and marl from the desert of 240 million years ago underlie the Vale. But from Northallerton south to Doncaster you won't see much of these rocks. They are easily eroded, and today they are mostly buried beneath a blanket of clay, sand, silt and gravel.

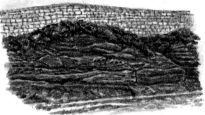

DONCASTER STATION. [SE 572 027] A wall of white magnesian limestone tops a cutting in soft red desert sandstone.

Gravel
Rock
Heather

To cross Pennine bogs, 'Blind Jack' had bundles of heather laid in rows, as a platform for the road.

As a young man, *Blind Jack of Knaresborough* (John Metcalf, 1717–1810), worked as a guide at Mother Shipton's Cave. He is better known for the 290 kilometres of new turnpike road that he surveyed and built in the north of England.

◄ **The Dropping Well, Mother Shipton's Cave, Knaresborough Gorge [SE 347 565]**
Waters, rich in minerals dissolved from the magnesian limestone, drop from the cliff. As the water evaporates it leaves a limy deposit, called tufa, on objects hung below.

Magnesian Limestone is crushed as roadstone and is also used in the chemical industry.

Jurassic Seas

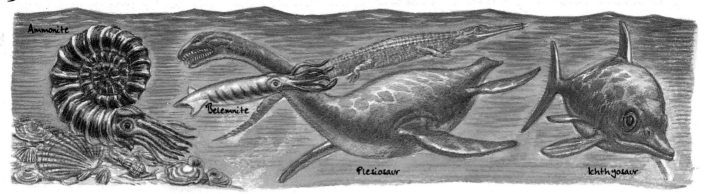

Ammonite
Belemnite
Plesiosaur
Ichthyosaur

Ammonites and belemnites swim in the shallow sea that covers Yorkshire in early Jurassic times. Their fossils, along with sea snails, oysters and scallops, are common in the mudstones, sandstones, limestones and ironstones deposited in the Jurassic period which started 210 million years ago. When the sea deepens, around 190 million years ago, plesiosaurs, sea crocodiles and ichthyosaurs move in. The bones of these large sea-going reptiles have been found in the Jet Rock and Alum Shales of the Yorkshire coast.

Alum quarry near Ravenscar. [NZ 969 017]

Ironstone was mined on the coast and in the North York Moors between 1848 and 1964. Ironstone layers, standing out pale and rusty against the dark shale, to produce banding like a liquorice allsort, can be seen in the cliffs east of Staithes.

Nodules form when lime or iron in sea bed sediments gathers around a centre of attraction. Some grow around shells. Most are rounded and no bigger then a tennis ball. Many look as if they have been squashed.

Alum was extracted from shale beds in conspicuous quarries that bite into the clifftops from Ravenscar to Boulby, and along the edges of the Moors. Alum is a salt used in tanning leather and dying cloth. It was extracted from Alum Shale by a complex process of burning, soaking, boiling and cooling. The industry lasted from around 1600 to 1871, when a new process allowed production to move to the coalfields.

Some bands of Jurassic ironstone, like the Pecten seam at Old Nab, Staithes [NZ 794 187], are crammed with fossil shells.

This WHALE STONE, a metre wide, is a limestone nodule from the cliff at Jet Wyke, Staithes. [NZ 792 188]

Baked alum shale with unbaked centre.

Fossilised Folk Tales

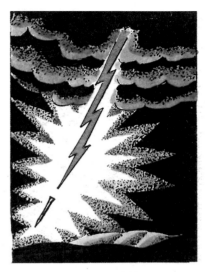

Devil's Toenails

The Devil left an enormous number of toenails along the Yorkshire coast! You will often find them on the beach washed down from nearby cliffs.

They are really the shells of *Gryphaea*, a relative of the clam and oyster, which lived on the seabed at a time when dinosaurs roamed the land.

The lines on the shell are growth rings, so you can estimate how old a 'toenail' was when it became fossilised. Ocassionally you will find both halves of *Gryphaea's* shell still joined together. One half was much larger than the other.

St Hilda's Snakes

Abbess Hilda rounded up the serpents that swarmed on the site of her Abbey at Whitby. As she hurled them from the clifftop each unfortunate snake lost its head.

'Snakestones' are actually the coiled fossil shells of **ammonites** (extinct relatives of squid and octopus). Most will fit in the palm of your hand, but they can be as small as a button or as big as a lorry tyre.

They are common along the Yorkshire coast. Local people carved heads on the 'snakestones' to make the resemblance to a serpent more convincing.

Thunderbolts

Bullet-shaped stones were said to be thunderbolts, found where lightning had struck the ground.

They are in fact the fossilised skeletons of *belemnites,* which were squid-like creatures. The fossil is the equivalent of the cuttlebone of the cuttlefish.

Belemnites were a favourite food of those great sea reptiles, the long-necked plesiosaur and the dolphin-like ichthyosaur. Tiny hooks from the belemnite's tentacles have been found amongst the fossilised stomach contents of these sea-going giants.

Dinosaur Delta MID-JURASSIC, 180 MILLION YEARS AGO

In mid-Jurassic times, a river system draining land to the north created a delta (Ravenscar Sandstone) in north Yorkshire which became home to many dinosaurs who left their tracks fossilised in the sand. Plants were washed down from higher ground.

Conifer

Monkey Puzzle

The mid-Jurassic plant beds of Yorkshire are renowned because they give us a glimpse of the vegetation of the period. Already in lower Jurassic times, branches of trees like the Monkey Puzzle were sometimes washed out to sea. Pieces that sank into dark, oily mud on the sea bed were preserved as jet, a kind of coal. Jet shale, in which most jet is found, smells of paraffin when a fresh piece is broken. Whitby Jet was famous in Victorian times when it was cut and polished to make black, shiny jewellery.

Jet

Tree Fern

Fern

Horsetails

Cycads

Tracking Dinosaurs

Thousands of dinosaur footprints have been found in Jurassic rocks between Ravenscar and Scarborough. These four dinosaurs, or species like them, contributed to these tracks.

Coelophysis is a small, fast, lightweight hunter, up to three metres long, armed with sharp claws and lots of saw-edged teeth.

Megalosaurus: nine metres long and weighing a ton, is strong enough to kill the big Jurassic plant-eating dinosaurs.

Cetiosaurus: this early sauropod dinosaur weighs as much as three large elephants and is as long as two buses. It has to eat enormous amounts of plants.

Camptosaurus is a plant-eater that can nip off tough fronds with its beak-like snout. It has a long tongue, fleshy cheeks and rows of crowned teeth adapted for its diet of tough plants.

Coral and Clay

Fossil 'shrimp' burrows in mid-Jurassic sandstone can be seen in some of the headstones in Whitby churchyard and on the foreshore. Weathering of the stones has left a cast of the infilled burrows. You can even see the claw marks made by the burrowing 'shrimps', but fossils of the creatures themselves have never been found.

White Horse of Kilburn [SE 511 813], on the south west scarp of the Hambleton Hills was cut in the turf in 1857 to reveal the calcareous sandstone below.. The Hambleton Hills, are, like the Tabular and Howardian Hills, topped by Corallian rocks of the Upper Jurassic. Because the sandstone is buff-grey it was whitewashed to make it more visible. In recent years crushed chalk from the nearby Wolds has been spread across it.

Coral Seas

OOLITE pellets grow as they become coated in more and more lime.

Oolite forms in warm shallow seas where specks of sand or shell fragments are swished around by the waves and are gradually coated with lime.

OOLITE is a limestone made up of tiny round grains of white calcite (lime), which looks like fish-roe.

The End of the Jurassic

Market Weighton Block ▶

The Jurassic rocks of north Yorkshire were laid down in a basin separated by a shallow ridge from the sea that covered south Yorkshire and the rest of England. The ridge, a stable block of rocks between the two basins, around the present site of Market Weighton, was itself often under water.

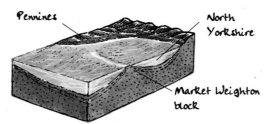

The remains of coral reefs are found in the Howardian Hills near Malton and make up the flat tops of the Tabular Hills between Helmsley and Scarborough. They can be seen along the coast from Cayton Bay to Filey Brigg.

Towards the end of the Jurassic the sea deepened. The soft Kimmeridge Clay from this period has been eroded to form the **Vale of Pickering** *(above)*, which lies between the Tabular Hills to the north and the Chalk Wolds to the south.

Jurassic Sandwich

JURASSIC 210–145 MILLION YEARS AGO

Yorkshire's Jurassic rocks are best seen in the sea cliffs from Staithes to Scarborough. They form the North York Moors along with the Hambleton Hills and Tabular Hills to the south.

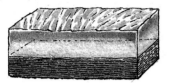

1. Liassic clays

2. Ravenscar sandstones

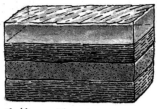

3. Kimmeridge clays

4. Alpine folding

North east Yorkshire, **190 million years ago**. Mud, later to form soft shale is laid down on the sea bed.

180 million years ago: there is uplift and sandstone is laid down by rivers draining from the north.

150 million years ago: the sea deepens and soft clays are deposited again.

25 million years ago: the Jurassic rocks are uplifted and gently folded into a shallow dome.

Tough mid-Jurassic Ravenscar sandstones cap the cliffs at **Port Mulgrave**. There are soft Liassic shales below.

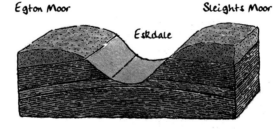

The same sandstones and Corallian rocks make up the tops of the **North York Moors**, the dales are carved deep into the softer Liassic shales that lie beneath.

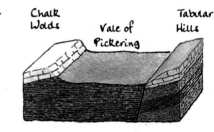

The **Vale of Pickering** lies on soft Kimmeridge Clay which dates from near the end of the Jurassic period.

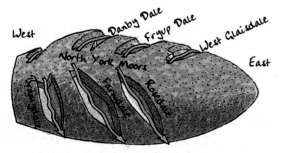

Rivers flow down the sides of the North York Moors dome. They have carved deep dales in the soft shales beneath.

At **Robin Hood's Bay** a dome can be seen in the Jurassic rocks. [NZ 958 035]

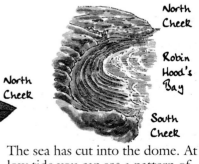

The sea has cut into the dome. At low tide you can see a pattern of curving layers of shale. The outer ring of tough sandstone forms the 'cheeks' at either end of the bay.

'Strata' Smith

William Smith, 1769–1839

1794, the Industrial Revolution. As canal mania sweeps the country, new cuttings slice through the rocks of England.

William Smith, age 25, a canal surveyor with the Coal Canal Company, is on his first visit to Yorkshire. He studies the layers of rock from the coalfield to York...

...as evening falls, he climbs York Minster tower...

...he sees the Chalk of the Wolds lying over the Jurassic and the soft red rock of the Vale of York: just as he had seen in the south of England.

Like so many slices of bread and butter!

Chalk
Jurassic
Red rock

Smith and company enjoy a 'good dinner and a pineapple' at the Black Swan...

...he had proved that stratigraphy, the study of rock layers, can be applied right across the country.

1809, Cuckfield, Sussex: Smith finds a dinosaur bone, the first to be included in a geological collection.

Iguanodon

Smith publishes the first geological map, of England and Wales, in 1815.

In 1832, while working as a land agent near Scarborough, Smith makes a map of the Hackness Hills.

Clay
Grit and Limestone
HACKNESS

The pattern of valleys reminds him of the antlers of a stag.

Woodland on steep poor soils over gritstone.

Fields on gentler clay slopes and valley bottom.

Gritstone (porous)
Spring line
Oxford Clay (impervious)

Springs which have cut these valleys occur at the gritstone/clay boundary.

40

Smith helps design the world's first rock and fossil museum...

...The Rotunda, Scarborough. It is built of limestone deposited in a warm Jurassic sea, quarried nearby at Hackness.

His nephew John Philips paints a section of the rocks of the Yorkshire coast.

The shelves are painted to match, so you can see where each rock comes from.

As in the cliffs, the fossils and rocks on the shelves are arranged in layers: oldest below, youngest above.

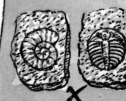

Smith's Laws

'Strata' Smith was also called the 'Father of English Geology'. He was the first to notice that fossils can help us recognise and date rocks.

Each layer or bed (stratum) of rock has its own set of fossils; generally the oldest beds are below, the youngest above.

Fossils are the remains of past life, not just freaks of nature.

Extinction is forever; when a fossil disappears from the record of the rocks, it never reappears.

If two different-looking rocks contain the same set of fossils, they must be the same age.

If two rocks look the same but contain different sets of fossils, they formed at different times.

Chalk Cliffs

At first glance Chalk seems to be exactly the same from one place to another. But the sea has found strong and weak points, carving out headlands and bays.

Bedding plane

Joint

Chalk was laid down on the bed of a warm clear sea when the last dinosaurs still roamed the Earth. Flat layers that were once the sea bed now make nesting ledges for razorbills, kittiwakes and gannets. These surfaces are called bedding planes.

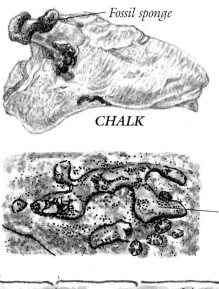

Fossil sponge

CHALK

Flints

Some layers of the chalk contain hard glassy nodules of **flint**. The yellow flints at Selwicks Bay follow the shape of the 'shrimp' burrows in which they formed. Flint is made of silica the same mineral as quartz crystals.

Shape of 'shrimp' burrow.

Yellow flint

Boulder Clay (till) lies on top of the cliffs at Flamborough. It was dumped on top of the chalk by glaciers during the last ice age.

Sea cave: erosion has picked out a weakness, such as a joint, in the chalk.

Blow-hole, a collapsed sea cave.

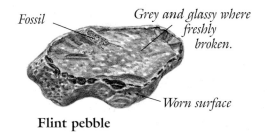

Sea stack, the remnant of a former cliff.

Illustration based on Selwicks Bay [TA 255 708]

Fossil

Grey and glassy where freshly broken.

Worn surface

Flint pebble

42

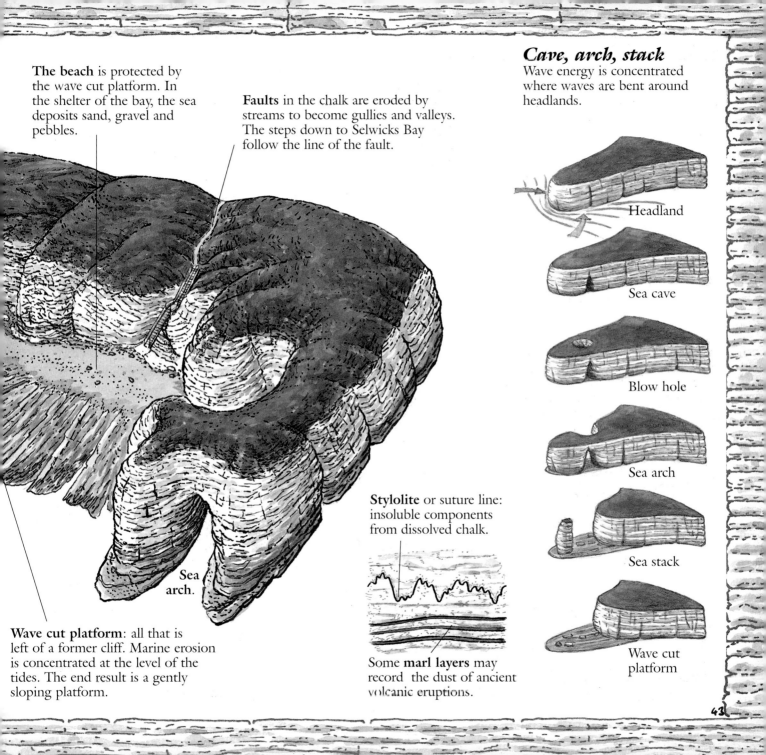

The beach is protected by the wave cut platform. In the shelter of the bay, the sea deposits sand, gravel and pebbles.

Faults in the chalk are eroded by streams to become gullies and valleys. The steps down to Selwicks Bay follow the line of the fault.

Sea arch.

Wave cut platform: all that is left of a former cliff. Marine erosion is concentrated at the level of the tides. The end result is a gently sloping platform.

Stylolite or suture line: insoluble components from dissolved chalk.

Some **marl layers** may record the dust of ancient volcanic eruptions.

Cave, arch, stack
Wave energy is concentrated where waves are bent around headlands.

Headland

Sea cave

Blow hole

Sea arch

Sea stack

Wave cut platform

Zoo in the Ooze

The **scallop**, *Euthymipecten*, has two rows of tiny eyes. If a starfish attacks it can 'hop' away by clapping its two shells together.

The **sea urchin** *Micraster* burrows in the ooze while another urchin, *Tylocidaris*, ambles across the sea bed, protected by club-shaped spines.

'Prawns' burrow in the soft chalky mud.

Spondylus, the **thorny oyster**, has spines which keep its shell opening clear of the ooze.

Life in the Chalk Sea

Tyrannosaurus rex rules the land, but Pangaea is fast breaking up. Sea level rises as volcanic activity along mid-ocean ridges increases. By 95 million years ago half the world's land is flooded. Marine life adapts to the chalky white ooze which covers the sea bed. At the end of this period, 65 million years ago, the dinosaurs vanished and many other land and marine animals became extinct.

The **sea lily** *Marsupites* rests directly in the mud. Unlike most others it has no stalk.

Sponges need a place where the ooze is firm enough for them to anchor.

A group of *Carneithyris* **brachiopods** anchor their stalks to shell fragments lying on the mud.

Chalk

Coccoliths in chalk ×500.

The white ooze is made up of tiny shells, or **coccoliths**, of single-celled plants that drifted in the plankton. Copepods, tiny crustaceans, eat these microscopic plants and their droppings, little pellets of coccolith shells, fall to the sea bed. Chalk, 99 per cent calcium carbonate, is made up of these tiny fossil shells.

The Wolds

On the Wolds, Yorkshire's chalk uplands, the soil is thin, reddish and dotted with chalk rubble. The red material is marl which is left when large quantities of chalk have been dissolved away. Dry valleys and rounded, rolling downs are typical of chalk country, since water soon finds its way underground. Some of the valleys were deepened in the Ice Age, and much of Yorkshire's chalk now lies beneath a blanket of Ice Age boulder clay, sand and gravel.

Earthy Tertiary   65–2 MILLION YEARS AGO

Yorkshire was land during this time, but events elsewhere had some repercussions

Atlantic Split

55 million years ago Europe and America are drifting apart.

There are volcanoes and lava flows on the new west coast of Scotland.

Molten rock fills long cracks underground.

The rock gradually cools to form a dyke.

The Cleveland Dyke stretches from Scotland to Yorkshire. It has been quarried for roadstone.

Quarry at Sil Howe near Goathland. [NZ 849 030]

North Sea Rift

The Atlantic split has already formed the North Sea by stretching and rifting

Rifting thins the Earth's crust producing faults and folds.

Heat at depth in the Earth 'cooks' the fossil remains of plants and animals...

Oil and gas forms and rises through spaces in the rocks above.

Rising oil and gas is trapped when it meets an impervious capping.

Alpine Crunch

25 million years ago...

As the Atlantic splits, Africa swings around and collides with Europe.

Alps

In a continental collision with Europe, the Alps and other fold mountains are thrown up.

Distant ripples of the Alpine collision cause folds and faults in Yorkshire's rocks.

The Pennines are uplifted along old lines of weakness.

45

Ice on the Rocks

QUATERNARY, TWO MILLION YEARS
AGO TO THE PRESENT DAY

The Quaternary has been called the
Ice Age. How does an ice age start?
Perhaps it was the change in ocean
currents and climate when drifting
continents gathered around the North
Pole. Wobbles in the Earth's orbit or
major periods of mountain building
may also help trigger cold periods.

450 000 years ago
Anglian Glaciation

During the last two million years,
ice sheets, perhaps over 1000 metres
thick, have moved across Yorkshire
on several occasions. During the
Anglian Glaciation the ice got as far
as north London and the whole of
Yorkshire was covered.

18 000 years ago
Devensian Glaciation

During the last of these main ice
advances, only parts of Yorkshire
were covered. All the ice features
shown on the next few pages date
from this last, Devensian, glaciation.
Most traces of the deposits of the
previous glaciations were wiped out
at this time.

Glaciated Yorkshire,
18 000 years ago

Valley glaciers in
the northern Dales

Calder Valley
was ice free

There was a glacier in Airedale but
Calderdale and other valleys to the
south were ice free.

North York Moors

North
Sea ice

Lake
Pickering

Vale of
York ice

Holderness

Lake
Humber

Much of the Pennines and
the North York Moors were
ice free. Ice squeezing
through a gap in the
Pennines at Stainmore
spread out over the Vale of
York. Ice from Scandinavia
filled up the North Sea and
even rode up over parts of
the coast.

Erratics

An erratic is a rock moved from its place of origin by ice.

One of the Norber greywacke erratics [SD 765 697]

The ice carried along rocks and boulders. When it melted the rocks were dumped, often far from where their journey had started. **Shap Granite** contains big rectangular crystals of feldspar. It formed in only one place, at the east side of the Lake District. Shap Granite boulders have been found in the Vale of York and on the Yorkshire coast. So we know that the ice must have flowed around the North York Moors. No Shap Granite boulders have been found on the moors themselves, which stood out like an island, almost surrounded by moving ice.

At Crummackdale, near Ingleborough, the ice plucked up boulders from Silurian rocks on the valley floor and dumped them on top of Norber, a nearby hill.

Glaciers normally flow downhill, but here the way out of the valley was blocked causing ice to ride over the limestone plateau. When the ice melted it left its boulders of greywacke from the valley floor scattered over the limestone pavement. Normally this type of greywacke is found beneath the Carboniferous Limestone.

Limestone dissolves in water. For 12 000 years the sandy greywacke boulders have acted as umbrellas. Slightly acidic water has dissolved the surrounding limestone pavement leaving each greywacke boulder perched on a remnant block some 30 centimetres high.

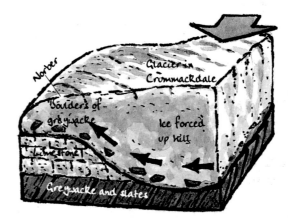

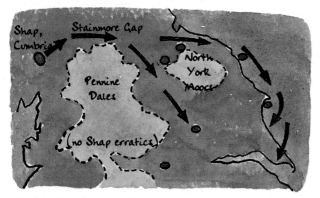

Tracking the Shap erratics.

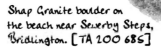

Shap Granite boulder on the beach near Sewerby Steps, Bridlington. [TA 200 685]

Between the Glaciations

The bones of hippopotamus were found at Wortley Brick Pits, Leeds, in 1852. They date from the last, or Ipswichian, interglacial period, 120 000 years ago.

Between the glaciations, it was often as warm as it is today, and sometimes warmer. Straight-tusked elephant, steppe bison, narrow-nosed rhinoceros and hippopotamus roamed across wooded grassland in Yorkshire.

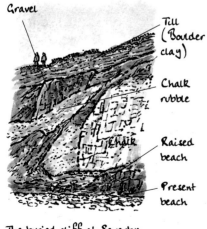

The buried cliff at Sewerby.

Gravel
Till (Boulder clay)
Chalk rubble
Chalk
Raised beach
Present beach

The Buried Cliff of Holderness [TA 197 683]

When the ice sheets melted, world sea level rose. During the Ipswichian interglacial period, the North Sea came farther inland than it does today. A chalk cliff stretched from Hessle near Hull to Sewerby near Bridlington. This old cliff line is now buried by the debris of the last ice advance. Near Sewerby Steps you can still see this prehistoric cliff, partly buried by boulder clay. At its foot is a raised beach, a metre above present day sea level.

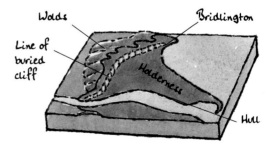

Wolds
Bridlington
Line of buried cliff
Holderness
Hull

Devensian glacial till has buried the interglacial cliff.

48

The Hyenas' Den

In 1821 the bones of hyenas, rhinos, hippos, bison and elephants were discovered in the mud on the floor of Kirkdale Cave, near Kirkbymoorside. [SE 678 856]

Today most of Kirkdale Cave has been quarried away.

The Rev. William Buckland (1784–1856), Professor of Geology at Oxford, came to examine the find. At first he thought that the animals had been washed into the cave during Noah's flood. But he noticed that all the bones had been broken and gnawed. He realised that the cave had been the lair of a pack of hyenas. They had dragged pieces of their prey in through the narrow entrance of the cave.

Buckland fed meat to captive hyenas and compared the resulting bones with those in the cave.

Victoria Cave [SD 838 651]

Victoria Cave, two kilometres north of Settle, was discovered by accident in the year of Queen Victoria's coronation when a dog scrambled into a hidden opening.

THE LAST (IPSWICHIAN) INTERGLACIAL, 120 000 years ago: hyenas use Victoria Cave as a den.

THE LAST ADVANCE OF THE ICE, some 18 000 years ago: ice blocks the cave entrance. Layers of clay are deposited in the flooded cave.

AFTER THE ICE, 10 000 years ago: stone age hunters use the cave, leaving tools of flint and reindeer bone.

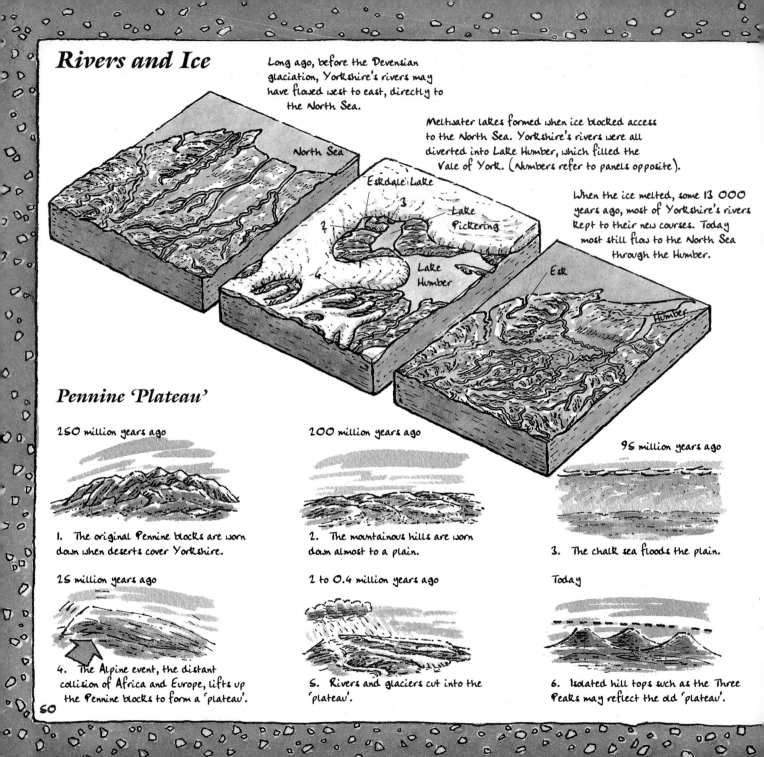

Rivers and Ice

Long ago, before the Devensian glaciation, Yorkshire's rivers may have flowed west to east, directly to the North Sea.

Meltwater lakes formed when ice blocked access to the North Sea. Yorkshire's rivers were all diverted into Lake Humber, which filled the Vale of York. (Numbers refer to panels opposite).

When the ice melted, some 13 000 years ago, most of Yorkshire's rivers kept to their new courses. Today most still flow to the North Sea through the Humber.

North Sea

Eskdale Lake

3

2

4

Lake Pickering

Lake Humber

Esk

Humber

Pennine 'Plateau'

250 million years ago

1. The original Pennine blocks are worn down when deserts cover Yorkshire.

200 million years ago

2. The mountainous hills are worn down almost to a plain.

95 million years ago

3. The chalk sea floods the plain.

25 million years ago

4. The Alpine event, the distant collision of Africa and Europe, lifts up the Pennine blocks to form a 'plateau'.

2 to 0.4 million years ago

5. Rivers and glaciers cut into the 'plateau'.

Today

6. Isolated hill tops such as the Three Peaks may reflect the old 'plateau'.

1   Lake Gormire meltwater channel

[NZ 514 830]

During the last advance of the ice, a glacier filled the Vale of Mowbray and the Vale of York. Water draining from the North York Moors flowed south between the edge of the moors and the ice sheet. At Sutton Bank the torrent cut a channel across the hillside. Lake Gormire now lies in the old channel.

2   Newtondale meltwater channel

[NZ 850 975]

The North York Moors Railway follows this deep channel cut by glacial meltwater from Eskdale Lake. After the glaciation the River Esk returned to its former course, reaching the sea at Whitby. Today no river runs the length of Newtondale.

3   Forge Valley

[SE 985 860]

The River Derwent used to flow to the sea near Scarborough. When that outlet was blocked by ice and debris, a lake formed in the valleys of the Hackness Hills, which overflowed cutting Forge Valley. When the ice melted the Derwent kept to its new course, making a detour of more than 150 kilometres to reach the sea at Spurn Head.

4

Knaresborough Gorge
[SE 349 570]

A lake formed when the original outlet of River Nidd was blocked by ice in the Vale of York. Overflowing water cut the gorge at Knaresborough. The Nidd still keeps to its new course through the gorge and into the next valley to the south.

Legacy of the Ice

When the last (Devensian) ice sheets melted, they left a thick blanket of clay, ground-up rock and boulders spread across the landscape. This material is called **till** or **boulder clay**. You can see it in the cliffs of Holderness, south of Bridlington.

Hornsea Mere
[TA 200 473]

Boulder Clay cliffs, Hornsea [TA 202 499]

Kettle Hole Lakes

Sometimes a large lump of ice was left lying amongst the debris. When it melted it left a hole in the blanket of boulder clay. This filled with water to become a kettle hole lake. There were several of them in Holderness but they have silted up and been drained and now only one, Hornsea Mere, remains.

The Anglo Saxon place name 'sea', for instance in Withernsea and Skipsea, actually refers to a lake.

Moraine

A glacier acts like a conveyor belt, moving rock from highlands to lowlands. If a glacier flows forward at the same rate as it melts a crescent-shaped mound of sand, clay and gravel builds up at its snout: a moraine.

Previous position of snout of glacier

End moraine

Meltwater streams

IS 000 YEARS AGO.

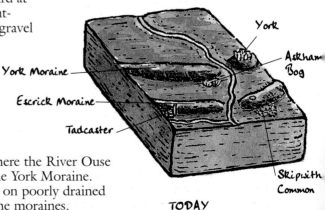

York

Askham Bog

York Moraine

Escrick Moraine

Tadcaster

Skipwith Common

TODAY

York is built where the River Ouse cuts through the York Moraine. Askham Bog is on poorly drained land between the moraines.

Drumlins

Drumlins are ice-carved piles of earth and rocks (till) that form small oval-shaped hills, each about 500 metres long. They can be seen at Ribblehead and between Gargrave and Settle. Drumlin country has been compared to a basket of eggs.

Before the last glaciation the River Ribble flowed east from Settle to the North Sea. Now that the way to Airedale is blocked by drumlins the Ribble turns south and flows to the Irish Sea.

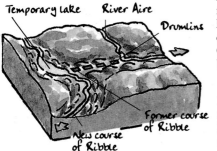

Drumlins near Hellifield [SD 578 556]

Ice flowed over the drumlin from the steep to the shallow end.

Glaciated Valley

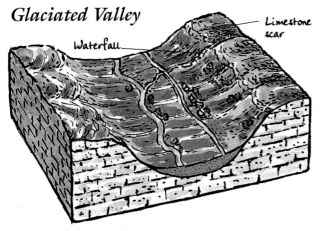

In the northern Dales, glaciers deepened the valleys, leaving them straightened out and U-shaped. Because the main valleys were deepened, streams feeding into them from the surrounding moors now have to plunge down in a series of waterfalls to reach the valley bottoms.

Dales farms typically have valley-bottom meadows, pasture on the slopes behind the farm, and access to summer grazing on the moorland above.

Meltwater Gorge

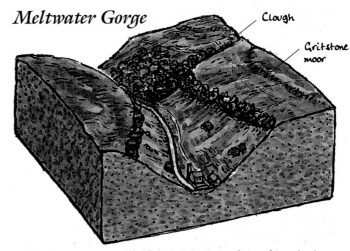

The Pennines south of Airedale were free of ice during the last advance. These valleys are V-shaped, cut by torrents of meltwater. The steep, narrow, side valleys, known as cloughs, were chosen as sites for water-powered woollen mills in the early years of the industrial revolution. When steam power arrived, larger mills were built on the floors of the main valleys.

53

Today's Vanishing Coast

Strip of coast lost since Roman times

The coast of Holderness, in the south east of Yorkshire, is retreating at an average rate of one to 1.5 metres a year. A strip of land five to six kilometres wide has been lost since Roman times. Whole villages, amongst them Auburn, Fraisthorpe, Hornsea Burton, Old Aldbrough and Old Kilnsea have vanished. Nowhere else in Europe is coastal erosion taking place at such a fast rate. An estimated two million tons of material are lost a year.

The cliffs of till (boulder clay) are unstable and collapse as landslips, especially when rainwater seeps into the ground.

The end of the road: boulder clay cliffs at Tunstall, near Withernsea. [TA 317 315]

Longshore Drift

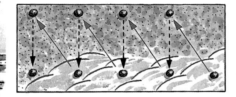

Groynes, or breakwaters, like these at Hornsea (ABOVE), slow down longshore drift and help retain the beach. The sea defences at Mappleton Sands (BELOW) are made up of boulders quarried in Scandinavia.

A good beach gives natural protection to a coast. The energy of the waves is used up by moving sand and pebbles along the beach in a process known as longshore drift. A pebble moves up the beach in the direction of the incoming tide (blue arrows). The weaker backwash, and gravity, roll it straight back down the slope (black arrows). In this way pebbles and sand are gradually moved from one end of the beach to another. A break in the supply of material, caused by the building of a breakwater for instance, may lead to the loss of the beach further down the coast, leaving the cliffs behind open to direct attack by the waves.

Backwash, Hornsea Beach.

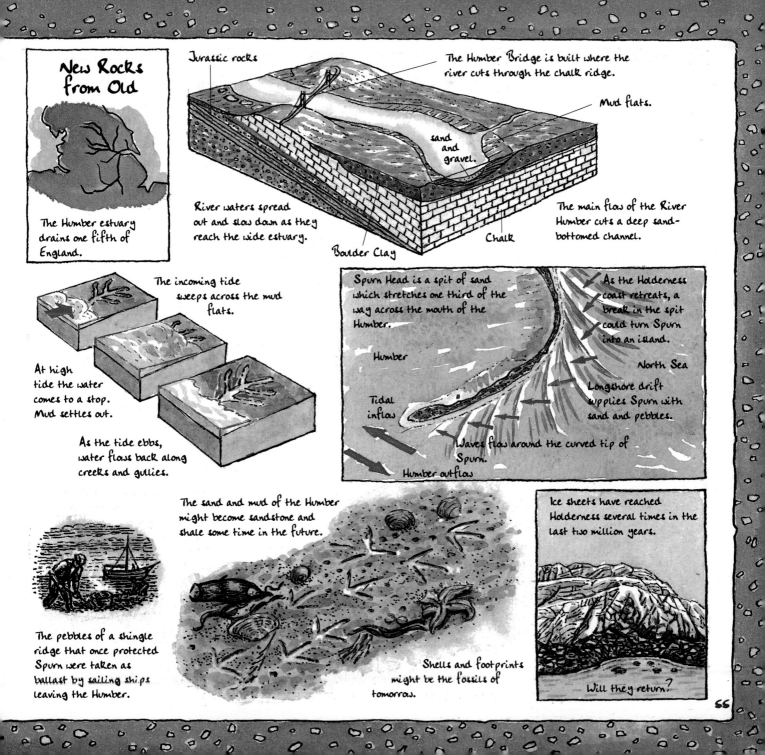

New Rocks from Old

The Humber estuary drains one fifth of England.

Jurassic rocks

The Humber Bridge is built where the river cuts through the chalk ridge.

Mud flats.

sand and gravel.

River waters spread out and slow down as they reach the wide estuary.

Boulder Clay

Chalk

The main flow of the River Humber cuts a deep sand-bottomed channel.

The incoming tide sweeps across the mud flats.

At high tide the water comes to a stop. Mud settles out.

As the tide ebbs, water flows back along creeks and gullies.

Spurn Head is a spit of sand which stretches one third of the way across the mouth of the Humber.

Humber

Tidal inflow

Humber outflow

As the Holderness coast retreats, a break in the spit could turn Spurn into an island.

North Sea

Longshore drift supplies Spurn with sand and pebbles.

Waves flow around the curved tip of Spurn.

The sand and mud of the Humber might become sandstone and shale some time in the future.

The pebbles of a shingle ridge that once protected Spurn were taken as ballast by sailing ships leaving the Humber.

Shells and footprints might be the fossils of tomorrow.

Ice sheets have reached Holderness several times in the last two million years.

Will they return?

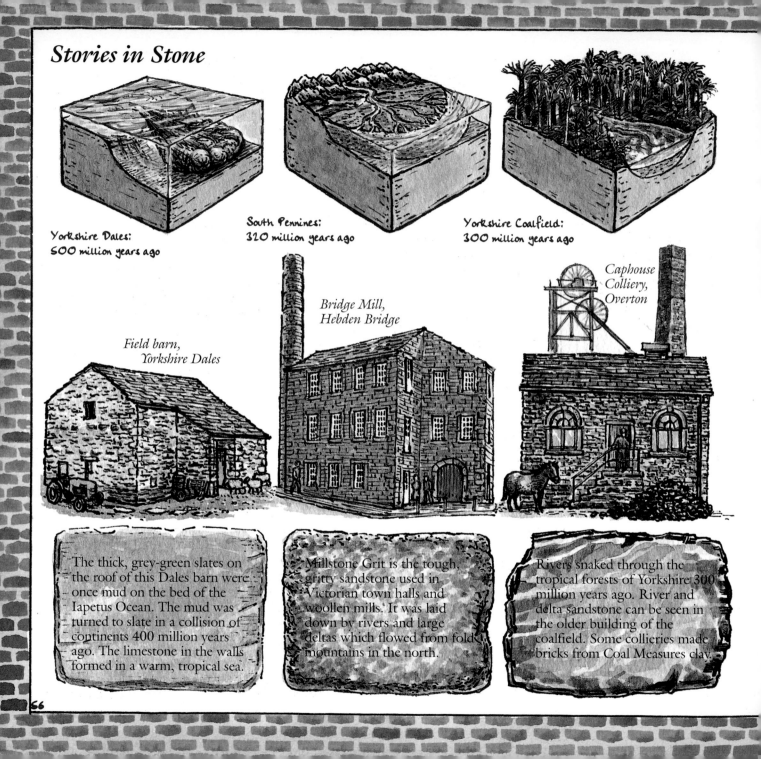

Stories in Stone

Yorkshire Dales:
500 million years ago

South Pennines:
320 million years ago

Yorkshire Coalfield:
300 million years ago

Field barn,
Yorkshire Dales

Bridge Mill,
Hebden Bridge

Caphouse
Colliery,
Overton

The thick, grey-green slates on the roof of this Dales barn were once mud on the bed of the Iapetus Ocean. The mud was turned to slate in a collision of continents 400 million years ago. The limestone in the walls formed in a warm, tropical sea.

Millstone Grit is the tough, gritty sandstone used in Victorian town halls and woollen mills. It was laid down by rivers and large deltas which flowed from fold mountains in the north.

Rivers snaked through the tropical forests of Yorkshire 300 million years ago. River and delta sandstone can be seen in the older building of the coalfield. Some collieries made bricks from Coal Measures clay.

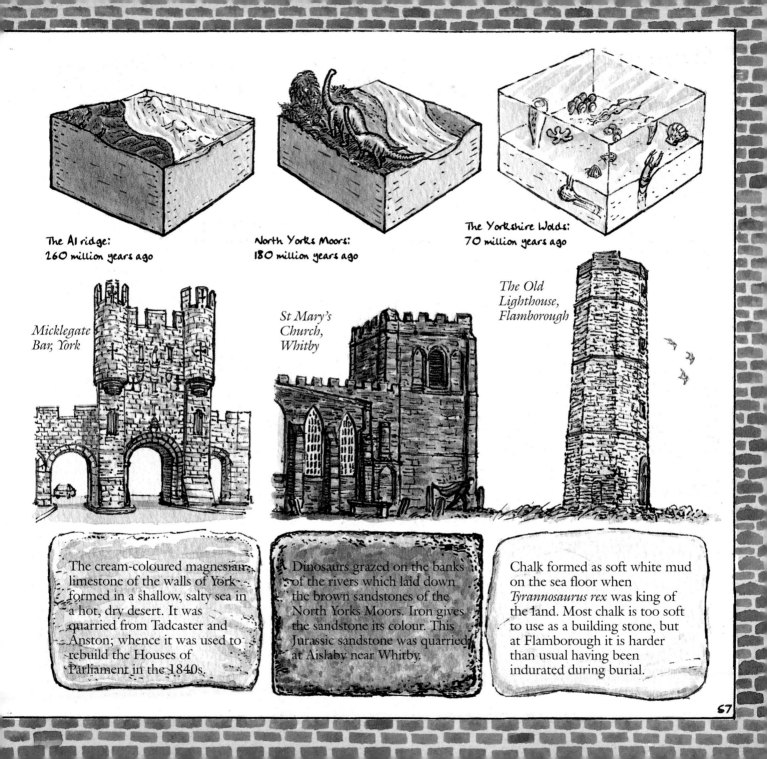

The A1 ridge:
260 million years ago

North Yorks Moors:
180 million years ago

The Yorkshire Wolds:
70 million years ago

Micklegate
Bar, York

St Mary's
Church,
Whitby

The Old
Lighthouse,
Flamborough

The cream-coloured magnesian limestone of the walls of York formed in a shallow, salty sea in a hot, dry desert. It was quarried from Tadcaster and Anston; whence it was used to rebuild the Houses of Parliament in the 1840s.

Dinosaurs grazed on the banks of the rivers which laid down the brown sandstones of the North Yorks Moors. Iron gives the sandstone its colour. This Jurassic sandstone was quarried at Aislaby near Whitby.

Chalk formed as soft white mud on the sea floor when *Tyrannosaurus rex* was king of the land. Most chalk is too soft to use as a building stone, but at Flamborough it is harder than usual having been indurated during burial.

57

Igneous Stone

Pumice stone is a porous, light volcanic rock.

Volcanic rocks form at the surface.

Granite forms deep underground.

All igneous rocks were once molten. The three shown here formed as molten masses in the roots of mountains. They have been polished to display their rock crystals.

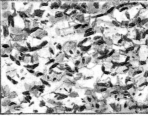
Granite can be speckled grey or pink.

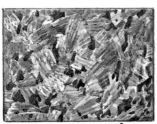
Larvikite contains iridescent feldspar crystals.

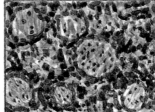
Rapakivi granite has round feldspar crystals.

Sedimentary Stone

Toothpaste contains powdered limestone.

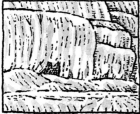
Travertine forms from lime-rich water.

Most sedimentary rocks are recycled: made of fragments, such as sand, mud and shells. Some limestones form by chemical reactions in hot springs.

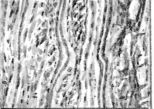
Travertine on McDonald's restaurants.

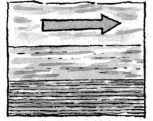
Most sediments are laid down by water.

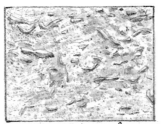
Portland Limestone contains fossil shells.

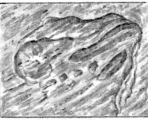
Flagstones split along shiny micas.

...tones

You can see rocks from all over the world in city centres

Graphite, used in pencil lead, and talc are metamorphic minerals

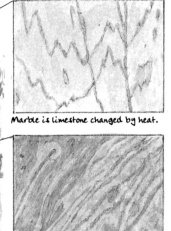

Marble is limestone changed by heat.

Metamorphic rocks are those that have been altered by heat and/or pressure. If a rock is completely re-melted it once more becomes an igneous rock.

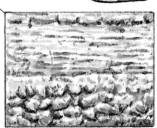

Green Lake District slate was volcanic ash.

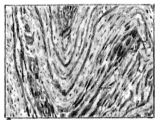

Banded gneiss has been partly re-melted.

Glass is made from silica sand.

Concrete is cement with sand and pebbles.

Portland cement, an early form of concrete, was invented by a Leeds bricklayer, Joe Aspdin (1778–1855). Cement is made from heated limestone mixed with clay or fly-ash.

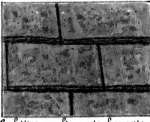

Brick, usually made from prehistoric clays.

Roof tiles, now often made of concrete.

Metamorphic Stone

Heat turns limestone to marble.

Pressure turns shale into slate.

Man-made Stone

Gravel: a big extractive industry.

Asphalt contains bitumen, derived from oil.

Of Further interest

Museums

Conisbrough: The Earth Centre
Doncaster Road, DN12 4DY.
(Tel: 01709 770566)

Doncaster Museum and Art Gallery,
Chequer Road, Doncaster DN12 2AE.
(Tel: 01302 734287)

Hawes: Dales Countryside Museum,
Station Yard, Hawes. (Tel: 01969 667494)

Huddersfield: Tolson Museum,
Ravensknowle Park, Wakefield Road,
Huddersfield HD5 8DJ.
(Tel: 01484 530591)

Keighley: Cliffe Castle Museum,
Spring Gardens Lane, Keighley BD20 6LH.
(Tel: 01535 758230)

**Kingston-upon-Hull City Museums and
Art Galleries,**
Town Docks Museum, Queen Victoria Square,
Kingston-upon-Hull HU1 3DX.
(Tel: 01482 610610)

**Leeds City Museum,
Municipal Building,** Calverley Street, Leeds
LS1 3AA. (Tel: 0113 2478275)

Overton: National Coal Mining Museum
Caphouse Colliery, New Road, Overton,
Wakefield WF4 4RH. (Tel: 01924 848806)

Rotherham: Clifton Park Museum,
Rotherham S65 2AA. (Tel: 01709 823635)

Scarborough: Woodend Museum,
The Crescent, Scarborough YO11 2PW.
(Tel: 01723 367326)

**Scunthorpe Borough Museum & Art
Gallery,**
Oswald Road, Scunthorpe, N. Lincs DN15
7BD. (Tel: 01724 843533)

Sheffield City Museum,
Weston Park, Sheffield S10 2TP.
(Tel: 0114 2768588)

Skipton: Craven Museum,
Town Hall, High Street, Skipton.
(Tel: 01756 794079)

York: Yorkshire Museum,
Museum Gardens, York YO1 2DR.
(Tel: 01904 629745)

National Park Information Centres

Yorkshire Dales National Park
Aysgarth Falls: (Tel: 01969 663424)
Clapham: (Tel: 015242 51419)
Grassington: (Tel: 01756 752774)
Hawes: (Tel: 01969 667450)
Malham: (Tel: 01729 830363)
Sedbergh: (Tel: 015396 20125)

The Sedgwick Geological Trail and the *Ingleton Waterfalls Trail* are published as two of the Yorkshire Dales National Park Trail Series.

The North York Moors National Park
The Moors Centre, Danby, N. Yorkshire
YO21 2NB. (Tel: 01287 660540)

The North York Moors National Park publish the *Ravenscar Trail Guide* and a leaflet describing *The geology of North Yorkshire and Cleveland Heritage Coast.*

Bracken Hall Countryside Centre,
Glen Road, Baildon, West Yorks.
(Tel: 01274 584140)

Brimham Rocks (Tel: 01423 780688)

Show Caves

Clapham's Ingleborough Cave,
Approx. a 30 minute walk from Clapham
village. (Tel: 015242 51242)

Stump Cross Caverns

Further Reading

The British Geological Survey publishes geological maps and memoirs covering the whole of Yorkshire. *Please contact the Sales Desk, British Geological Survey, Keyworth, Nottingham NG12 5GG (Tel: 0115 936 3241).*

BRUMHEAD, D. 1979. *Geology explained in the Yorkshire Dales and on the Yorkshire Coast* David & Charles, Newton Abbot.

EDWARDS, W and TROTTER, F M. 1954. *British Regional Geology, The Pennines and Adjacent Areas.* HMSO, London.

FLETCHER, D. 1982. *Setting the Scene.* Pennine Heritage Network.

KENDALL, P F and WROOT, H E. 1924. *The Geology of Yorkshire.* Printed privately.

KENT, SIR PETER. 1980. *British Regional Geology, Eastern England from the Tees to the Wash.* HMSO, London.

LEWIS, DAVID B. 1991. *The Yorkshire Coast.* Normandy Press.

RAWSON, P F and WRIGHT, J K. 1992. *Geologists' Association Guide No.34, The Yorkshire Coast.* The Geologists' Association.

RAYNER, D H, and HEMINGWAY, J E. 1974. *The Geology and Mineral Resources of Yorkshire.* Yorkshire Geological Society.

SCRUTTON, C. 1994. *Yorkshire Rocks and Landscape, A Field Guide.* Ellenbank Press.

STAINFORTH, A. 1990. *Geology of the North York Moors.* North York Moors National Park Information Service.

WALTHAM, T. 1987. *Karst and Caves in the Yorkshire Dales National Park.* Yorkshire Dales National Park.

WILSON, ALBERT. 1992. *Geology of the Yorkshire Dales National Park.* Yorkshire Dales National Park.

Acknowledgements

Richard Bell would like to thank: Alison Armstrong, Barbara Bell, Gaynor Boon, Alan Brandon, Ian Chisholm, Tony Cooper, Paul Ensom, Siobhan Kirrane, Richard Myerscough, Adrian Norris, Jim Nunney, Anne Pennington-George, John Powell, Tom Whitfield, Tom Williams, Albert Wilson and Graham Woodrow.

Index

Yorkshire Rock Time Line

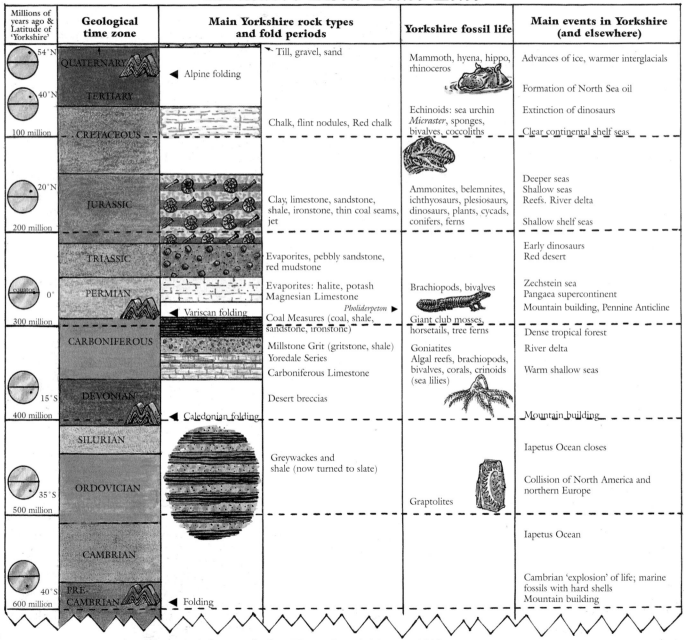

Millions of years ago & Latitude of 'Yorkshire'	Geological time zone	Main Yorkshire rock types and fold periods	Yorkshire fossil life	Main events in Yorkshire (and elsewhere)
54°N	QUATERNARY	Till, gravel, sand	Mammoth, hyena, hippo, rhinoceros	Advances of ice, warmer interglacials
40°N	TERTIARY	◀ Alpine folding		Formation of North Sea oil
100 million	CRETACEOUS	Chalk, flint nodules, Red chalk	Echinoids: sea urchin *Micraster*, sponges, bivalves, coccoliths	Extinction of dinosaurs / Clear continental shelf seas
20°N	JURASSIC	Clay, limestone, sandstone, shale, ironstone, thin coal seams, jet	Ammonites, belemnites, ichthyosaurs, plesiosaurs, dinosaurs, plants, cycads, conifers, ferns	Deeper seas / Shallow seas / Reefs. River delta / Shallow shelf seas
200 million	TRIASSIC	Evaporites, pebbly sandstone, red mudstone		Early dinosaurs / Red desert
equator 0°	PERMIAN	Evaporites: halite, potash Magnesian Limestone / ◀ Variscan folding	Brachiopods, bivalves *Pholiderpeton* ▶	Zechstein sea / Pangaea supercontinent / Mountain building, Pennine Anticline
300 million	CARBONIFEROUS	Coal Measures (coal, shale, sandstone, ironstone) / Millstone Grit (gritstone, shale) Yoredale Series / Carboniferous Limestone	Giant club mosses, horsetails, tree ferns / Goniatites / Algal reefs, brachiopods, bivalves, corals, crinoids (sea lilies)	Dense tropical forest / River delta / Warm shallow seas
15°S	DEVONIAN	Desert breccias / ◀ Caledonian folding		Mountain building
400 million	SILURIAN	Greywackes and shale (now turned to slate)		Iapetus Ocean closes
500 million	ORDOVICIAN		Graptolites	Collision of North America and northern Europe
	CAMBRIAN			Iapetus Ocean
600 million	PRE-CAMBRIAN	◀ Folding		Cambrian 'explosion' of life; marine fossils with hard shells / Mountain building

Formation of the Earth: 4600 million years ago

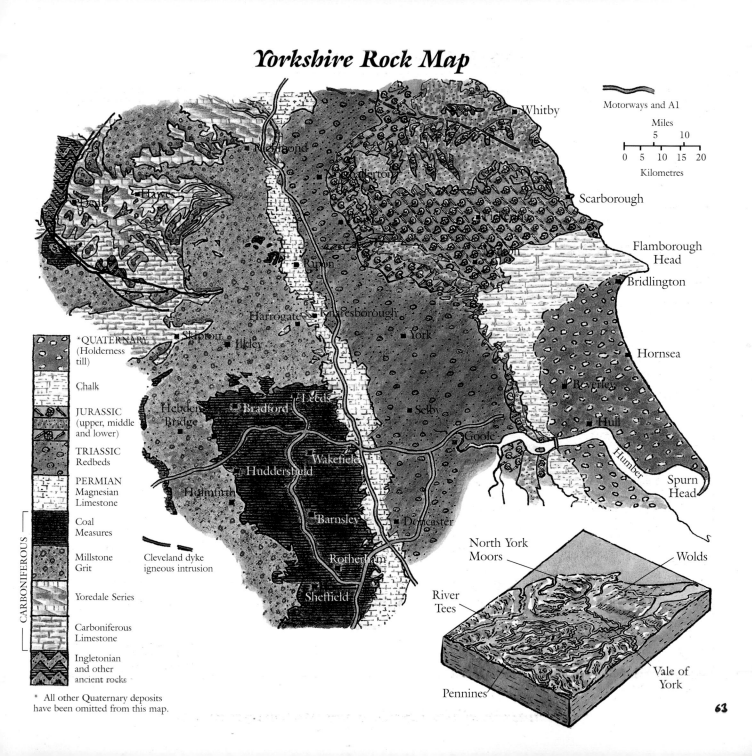

Yorkshire Rock Map

Motorways and A1

Miles
5   10
0   5   10 15 20
Kilometres

Whitby

Richmond

Northallerton

Scarborough

Hawes

Flamborough
Head

Bridlington

Ripon

Harrogate

Knaresborough

York

Hornsea

Skipton

Ilkley

Beverley

Hebden
Bridge

Bradford

Leeds

Selby

Hull

Holmfirth

Wakefield

Huddersfield

Goole

Humber

Spurn
Head

Barnsley

Doncaster

Rotherham

Sheffield

Legend

*QUATERNARY
(Holderness till)

Chalk

JURASSIC
(upper, middle and lower)

TRIASSIC
Redbeds

PERMIAN
Magnesian
Limestone

Coal
Measures

Millstone
Grit

Yoredale Series

Carboniferous
Limestone

Ingletonian
and other
ancient rocks

CARBONIFEROUS

Cleveland dyke
igneous intrusion

* All other Quaternary deposits
have been omitted from this map.

North York
Moors

Wolds

River
Tees

Pennines

Vale of
York

63

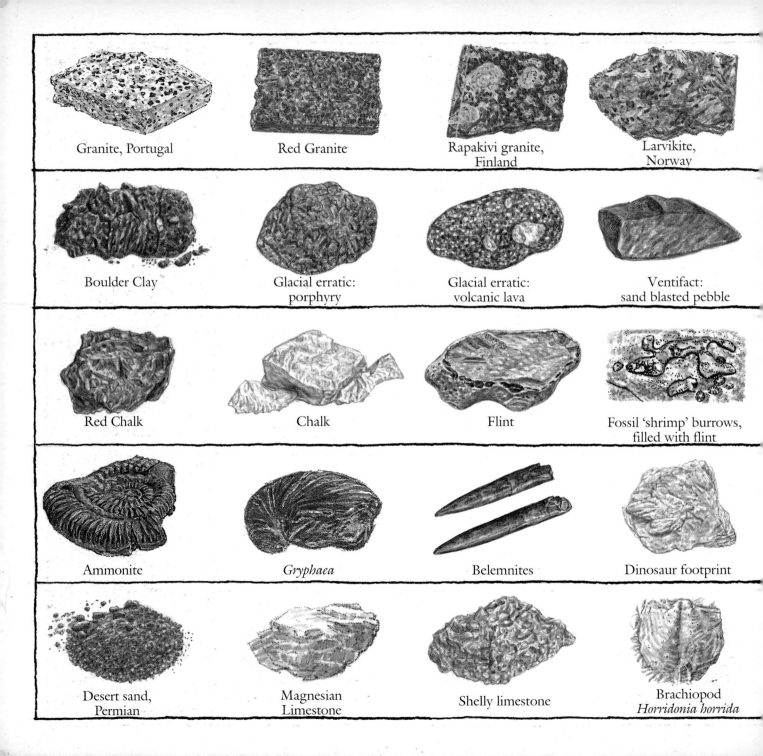

Granite, Portugal

Red Granite

Rapakivi granite, Finland

Larvikite, Norway

Boulder Clay

Glacial erratic: porphyry

Glacial erratic: volcanic lava

Ventifact: sand blasted pebble

Red Chalk

Chalk

Flint

Fossil 'shrimp' burrows, filled with flint

Ammonite

Gryphaea

Belemnites

Dinosaur footprint

Desert sand, Permian

Magnesian Limestone

Shelly limestone

Brachiopod
Horridonia horrida